Books by

ALISTAIR COOKE

A GENERATION ON TRIAL:
U.S.A. V. ALGER HISS (1 9 5 0 ; 1 9 5 2)

ONE MAN'S AMERICA (1 9 5 2)

CHRISTMAS EVE (1 9 5 2)

These are Borzoi Books
published by ALFRED A. KNOPF *in New York*

CHRISTMAS EVE

ILLUSTRATED BY MARC SIMONT

ALFRED · A · KNOPF

New York

Christmas Eve

by ALISTAIR COOKE

L. C. catalog card number: 52-12942

THIS IS A BORZOI BOOK,
PUBLISHED BY ALFRED · A · KNOPF, INC.

FIRST EDITION

NOTE

TO THE CHOSEN READER

These stories, which are all true so far as I know, were written for reading aloud, as stories were always meant to be. They were given by me as broadcasts, on three successive Christmas Eves, in a series of weekly talks called "Letter from America," which are spoken in New York and heard in Britain.

Any similarity between the characters of these tales and people living or dead is a simple, and acceptable, tribute to the accuracy of my reporting.

They are meant for children of all ages.

A. C.

CHRISTMAS EVE

ONE

IN the middle of Rockefeller Plaza, in the middle of
New York City, there is at Christmas time a great tree
about seventy feet high. It is said to be a Norway fir, but
by the time they have sprayed it with a fireproof silver
paint it looks like something between a redwood and a
giant aspen. It is fitted out with several thousand light

bulbs and leads strangers to America to complain about the "commercializing" of Christmas. But the practice of eating, drinking, and making merry at Christmas time is an entirely pagan idea, and it was on that ground that the early colonists of New England forbade their flock to drink

a mug of beer. They even resented the success of blasphemers in monkeying around with the calendar so as to make an unholy feast coincide with the birth of Jesus. One of the good Yorkshiremen on the *Mayflower* who kept a diary noted with some pride that the first day everybody was off the boat, the first day of digging the foundations of the Plymouth colony, was Christmas Day. He mentions that there was no pause for any nonsense like carols or dancing and adds the comment: "because what day soever our Lord was born, most certainly it was not the twenty-fifth of December."

But the Puritans lost out, in this as in many other things. Christmas has become a cheerful jumble of pious and heathen customs. And in New York the big tree in Rockefeller Plaza is the proper meeting-point of a pagan and a holy Christmas, for it magnificently combines electricity with a Gothic spire.

It was at this tree, a year ago, that Santa Claus got into trouble.

The real name of Santa Claus, by the way, is Zebby Adams. He lives in an old folks' home. I can't say for sure what the Zebby stands for. He may have been christened Zebah or Zebedee, but most likely it was Zebulun, one of those Biblical first names which are very common still in New England and the Midwest and which make so many unlikely-looking Americans sound like seventeenth-century bishops.

Zebby Adams entered the old folks' home up near Riverside Drive shortly after Pearl Harbor, because he lost a son in the First World War and got depressed at the prospect of another generation of lost sons. He had been a small-town banker in Massachusetts and was wiped out in the 1929 crash. He was a widower by then and had few relatives. He was also one of that strange breed of people—who will be with us, I fear, for a few years yet— who refuse charity and are too proud to seek out a helping hand. His house had been attached in January 1930 for debts he could not pay. And he took a bus a couple of hundred miles down to New York and lived anonymously for ten years or more doing odd and humble jobs. He lived in a little rented room and saved a few dollars whenever he could. Having lost his faith in the banking system, he kept his savings in a miniature mahogany desk, a Christmas present he had had as a child. He kept this money for the day when he would feel the first twinge of old age in the form of a sudden backache, an ominous stiff hand, or whatever it might be. He had a plan for this money.

One morning a few years ago he woke up and felt very tired. It was like no tiredness he had ever known and he knew in the instant of waking that he had passed over into old age. It was time to put his plan into action.

He went to the tiny desk and opened its drawers. There were bills of all denominations stuffed in there. He took them out and unfolded them and counted up to four hundred dollars. He put them in his pocket and went off to the old folks' home. He said it was a contribution. He said he could no longer keep up the rent of his room and wished to be taken in. They asked him for some credentials, and he pulled out a worn little card, a membership card in some forgotten club, which read: "Zebulun Adams, banker."

[7]

The officials at the home took this badly. But after a day or two, and some discreet telephone calls to the rather surprised inhabitants of the small town in Massachusetts, they took him in. He is there today.

Now, Zebby, a gentle blue-eyed man with tiny hands and a portliness that failed to fill out a frail-looking body, had long had a secret ambition. It was to be Santa Claus. He did it at the old folks' home two years in a row. It satisfied the old folks, some of whom doubted there was any such person. But it didn't satisfy Zebby. It only whetted his appetite. Then one October he read in the paper about a school or college way up the Hudson, in upstate New York: a college for Santa Clauses. It offered a two-weeks course and guaranteed to train and qualify "Master Santa Clauses" for employment in the big city department stores. "A calling," the advertisement said, "that has for too long been left to the amateur and the well-meaning bum." Zebby Adams felt a wince of conscience on both scores and resolved to qualify as a professional, so that he might look people, no matter how young, clear in the eye. He told the treasurer of the home that he needed one hundred and fifty dollars, which was the fee for the course and bed and board, and offered to repay it from his earnings in Christmas week. After a little niggling and finagling he got it. He wrote off to the college, received an application blank, filled it out, registered, and on the first day of December was on a train whistling up the Hudson.

He had the time of his life. He had always loved children and he had a way with them. He took them for what they were—cobras or tigers, say—and it never occurred to him in all his life to try to influence them, or mold them, or show them what was what. But like many another man with a special skill he was troubled by what he didn't know, and was unaware of the glaring fact that he was already superior to most people around him. He therefore applied himself with much zest and humility to learning what the college had to teach. He never missed a class. The first course was in "Greeting the Child," and he got an A for that in four days flat (on the third day he turned into the teacher). "Personal Cleanliness in the Role of Santa Claus" was something else he had no trouble with: his family had been Episcopalians and, having boasted of venerable connections with the carpenters and butchers who came over on the *Mayflower*, they had very genteel notions about personal appearance, combing the hair, and what coat ought to go with what pair of pants. To be precise, Zebby was a Harvard man, but in ordinary civilized intercourse he always kept a decent secret of it.

[9]

There was an afternoon class in "Problems of Denial" which puzzled him sorely. He discovered to his horror that department stores do not give away the gorgeous articles they bait the children with, and he shed a sneaking tear when he learned the correct answers to the quiz on this course. "Santa Claus: Father Substitute or Father Rival?" almost threw him, for it was his understanding that Santa Claus was a benefactor dropped from the skies who was practically honor-bound not to get mixed up with the female of the species. "That," said the instructor snappishly, "is not the point. It is what you mean to the little one that matters." That, said Zebby, was the way he'd always understood it. He got a B in this course, until he memorized a page from a psychology or geometry book—

he can't now remember which—and passed up into the select company of the A's.

He did very well in everything and at the end he impatiently took the train back to the city, carrying his bag and the special comb, make-up kit, and beard-deodorizing spray the college gave you along with your certificate. He also bore a letter to the personnel manager of a big midtown department store. For ten days he was a sensation with the young and a cause of misgiving to the floor manager, for in spite of his professional training he tended in an emergency to trust his instincts. He more than earned his loan from the old folks' home, however, and on Christmas Eve he picked up his check and left the store. He was happy and he was sad. He was also, I forgot to say, dressed in his scarlet costume—a gift from the well-contented store. He wanted to prolong his role and he conveniently forgot to change into street clothes. Instead, he showered moth flakes on his ordinary suit and carefully packed it away in his bag.

He went to a restaurant near by and was such a warming sight that strangers bought him drinks. A waiter insisted on sneaking him a stein of "heeltaps," the leavings of orders of brandy, whisky, champagne, and beer, to which the kitchen help used to add a little spice and sugar and brew it into a powerful punch.

When Zebby Adams left the restaurant it was very late and I'm afraid he was not himself. He started to march uptown swinging his bag; all the tiredness of his new-found old age had magically disappeared. He suddenly thought of the tree in Rockefeller Plaza and hurried to bask in its genial blaze. He was going at a fine pace by the time he reached Forty-second Street, and seeing the lonely lions outside the Public Library he stopped and serenaded them

with a favorite carol. "The Holly and the Ivy," he sang, "in Rocky-feller Plaza." By the time he came in sight of the British Empire Building he heard the three notes of the National Broadcasting Company pealing out on the midnight clear. They were sounding, in fact, the witching hour. And as they died on the air, the big tree suddenly went out. The only colored light in the Plaza came from the roof of a taxi waiting for a fare.

This was the fatal moment in the old age of Zebby Adams. For the little yellow light revived another long-buried ambition, which he was sure a reindeer now reminded him of. It was to drive a cab. He pattered over to the driver.

"My good fellow!" he cried.

"Listen," said the driver, "this is Christmas Eve. I ain't nobody's good fellow. I'm a Democrat."

The driver also wasn't himself, though it was true he was a Democrat. Zebby, however, leaned against the cab and put his head through the window. He told his secret to the driver.

"I couldn't do a thing like that," the driver said. "Liable to get my head broke, or a ticket or somepn."

"Only sit by my side," Zebby pleaded. "I will be a learner. You can be my sponsor, my guide. The traffic-bureau regulations permit it."

"Well—" said the driver, weakening.

Zebby saw his chance and almost lulled the driver to sleep with a flood of persuasive eloquence. He imagined the sheer sensual pleasure of flying past all the lighted trees of Park Avenue "without let or hindrance." He acknowledged the "enormous Christian favor" he was begging. More than that though, he argued, it would represent "a deep symbolic act." The driver bounced awake at the word "symbolic." He liked it.

"Is that what it would be, symbolic?" he asked.

"Nothing less," said Zebby, stroking his beard with one hand and pointing to the stars with the other.

"You sure?"

"Certain of it."

The driver jumped out on his side and came around the cab. He pulled the door wide open. He pointed to the steering wheel and bowed low. "Santa," he said, "it's all yours." (This was one of those historic sentences, like "I see no retreat" and "Don't shoot till you see the whites of their eyes.")

Santa hopped in and banged the door. He ground into first gear. He behaved like Zebby Adams on the crosstown street; but once he turned uptown and saw the splendid highway of Park Avenue ahead and its dancing lights, and not a human anywhere, he got the authentic high sign from the reindeer that had whispered to him in the Plaza. He put his foot way down, and as the lights winked from green to red, Santa flew on. A Cadillac screamed to a stop at Fifty-ninth Street as it slid across the avenue when the light changed. Through the Sixties the crosstown streets flashed by like the ribs of a fan. "Hot Diggety!" cried Santa. And they flew on.

They didn't fly very far before they heard behind them a sound of bells.

"Donner and Blitzen," shouted Santa, "they are with us still."

"You know them poissonally?" asked the driver with a little anxiety.

"Splendid fellows both," roared Santa.

It was not, however, the reindeer. It was a cop.

When they came into night court, the man on the bench looked stonily down at Zebby. Then he sighed and bent over a book with a pencil.

"Name?" he asked.

"Adams, Zebulun."

The judge wrote it down without a comma.

"Trade or profession?" he said, looking at his book.

"Santa Claus," said Zebby. "Master Santa Claus— M.S.C."

The judge scraped at his teeth with a fingernail.

"Five days in jail," he said. "Have you anything to say for yourself?"

"Merry Christmas, your Honor," Zebby said.

"— and five days for contempt of court," the judge added.

"And a happy New Year," said Santa.

The judge paused. He put his thumbnail to his teeth again and this time he rescued a shred of beef.

"Sentence suspended," said the judge.

The cabdriver took Zebby away uptown and drew up before an iron gate. He went round and opened the door on the passenger's side and led Zebby to the gate. He kissed him twice on both cheeks. "Bon sewer, mon general," he said, and opened up the gate and Zebby trotted up the path of the old folks' home. He stopped at the door and looked back.

"Au revoir, mon colonel," cried Zebby.

TWO

O F all the items about Christmas that come out in the newspapers none can be more heartbreaking to people who live in northern countries than a story that was flashed a couple of years ago from San Gabriel, California. The children of San Gabriel suffer under the handicap, when Christmas comes round, of never having any snow to frolic in. Their plight is all the more pathetic in that they can look up to the Sierra Madre mountains and see snow on the peaks for a good part of the year. But it doesn't come down into the foothill towns. And the San Gabriel chamber of commerce therefore decided one year to import it. They ordered snow machines from a Hollywood studio and fed into them fifty thousand pounds of ice, instead of the more normal element of snow-making, which, as everybody knows, is cornflakes. They hired studio technicians to make a snowstorm over a plot fifty by a hundred feet, in which at last the sun-tanned moppets rollicked and romped and came into their birthright.

We have not had much call to pity Hollywood in the last few years. But this is a time of Christian charity, and I think we can all feel decently sorry for any tribe of English-speaking people who inherit our Christmas literature and customs and who yet have never wallowed in the snow. Until San Gabriel redressed this grievance, it was the custom (I am told) for movie stars to gather the tots on the lawn, nestle close in two-piece bathing suits, have Father open a familiar volume and, in a strong clear voice across the swimming pool, begin to read about Scrooge and Marley's ghost. Their condition reminds me of the hero of the story I am about to tell.

His story never would have happened but for two things. He too had never seen a snowy Christmas. And he had a failing of character with which I for one happen to sympathize very much: he was always late, everywhere. It was so bad with him, and he came so close to losing his job so many times, that one day he took himself off to a psychiatrist. At the end of two years they discovered together that his trouble was deep and dire. He was a first-generation Californian—which is a fighting role in itself. But in his case it all went back to his mother, a New Englander who had married a man much older than herself, an Iowa farmer who retired and took his bride off to Long Beach, which was being advertised in the early 1920's as a sort of halfway house to paradise. They had two children. First a boy, the hero of this story. His mother insisted on christening him Learned, because when he was born she was already beginning to miss New England and in her childhood she had once met Judge Learned Hand at a party in Albany and admired him greatly. Two years later they had a girl and she was christened the comparatively normal Abigail, after her grandmother, and *her* grandmother, and *her* grandmother.

Learned was an impossible name to shout or even to say over a telephone. So the mother soon settled for the nickname he'd picked up—Larry. When our story begins, Larry had just spent three thousand dollars and two years on a couch (he got up for mornings, evenings, and meals) finding out why he resented being a Californian. That, it seems, was at the root of his unpunctuality. If you are still with me, I can tell you why. He found out that he had a yearning he had never admitted, even to himself (imagine!), for the places he had never seen and for all the things his mother got tearful about in the year she spent in bed before she died. Things like American elms, and the scarlet maples in the fall, and the smell of skunks, and the taste of Indian corn pudding, and the sight of white colonial churches rising from the snow. Larry had cruelly ridiculed these things and had spent most of his youth proving to his mother that he was a true barbarian by swimming in January, praising the smell of pine, oranges, and oil-derricks, drooling over superduper jumbo malteds and the California girls, and calling the first course of any meal a "starter."

Well, all this, it seems, was so much eyewash (the psychiatrist was a man from Hamburg who didn't like hamburgers) and sprang from nothing more complicated than a bad conscience. He made it up to himself and his origins by being late on all occasions. That is to say, he secretly despised the Californians for being his neighbors and insulted them to prove it.

That may sound a little queer as a basis for unpunctuality (his mother always insisted he was unpunctual because he didn't get started soon enough). But the psychiatrist believed it and Larry believed it. And that is the main thing.

Shortly after Larry got up from the couch for good, it

was Thanksgiving. And Hollywood put on its usual pre-Christmas parade. While he was watching a little Santa Claus on stilts, and big bathing beauties treading on cornflakes, he was suddenly seized with a bitter, bright longing to see snow, to live with it, to go East and see some snow. He decided then and there that he would spend Christmas in Connecticut. He would telephone his sister and beg her to take him in.

You will have gathered by now that he and his sister were orphans. But what I forgot to tell you was that his sister no longer lived in Hollywood. One day, just before she graduated from Hollywood High School, she went and sat on that famous drugstore stool where Lana Turner had been spotted and grabbed for immortality. And a sharp little man came up and said: "My, my." And a week later she was getting a screen test. She was an excessively pretty girl but nothing came of it. But being a New Englander she had pioneer blood in her veins. She decided to go East. "Go East, young woman," she said to herself, "and try out for television." She was a steady success in New York. By winking every evening in close-up she sent up the sales of one brand of nylons thirty-four and three-quarter per cent over all other brands of nylons. There was now no social world she could not inhabit. And one evening she met the advertising man who handled this nylon account. And they were married. He had a place in Connecticut. And so she, a simple soul, settled down on the soil of her forebears without having felt any of her brother's intermediate complications, like unpunctuality or the laying out of three thousand dollars.

She had been there nearly two years when our story begins. Larry was doing well with a movie company. He had done a three-year stretch in the army and wound up on a Pacific atoll in the camouflage corps. There was nothing on this coral strip to camouflage, since every spit of sand and scarlet fish that swam could be easily seen from the air. So for a year he sat in a shade temperature of a hundred and three and painted water-colors and read up books on art, which his sister sent him. The first batch that arrived happened to be, by a cheerful mistake of his sister's, all about the history of furniture. He asked for more. And when he got back home he went into the art department of one of the major studios as a technical adviser on period furniture. He was young—twenty-four—but he was smart and accurate and fast with his sketches. If he had not been, his unpunctuality would have had him fired. But he could scare up a Louis XVth chair, or draw in a portcullis on a backdrop, faster than anybody else. He was inconspicuous and friendly on the set, the sort of quiet cultivated expert who is known to illiterate movie stars as a useful drone.

So this is the cast of characters. A pretty sister, gone back East and married to a solid citizen, a television-account executive with a charming house in a small town on the Housatonic River. And Larry, young and lank, and charming in a forgetful way, living alone in Hollywood and, at the moment we first come on him, staring at the Thanksgiving Parade and thinking about snow. He brooded about it for a while and dismissed it as moonshine. But as it came nearer to Christmas there were heavy falls of snow reported in the East. The picture he was working on looked as if it would be all shot and done with before Christmas. So one week before Christmas Eve, in the early evening, he couldn't wait to get home and put in a call to his sister. Like most unpunctual people he rarely wrote letters but used the telephone at all times. The long-distance telephone is so miraculously run in America, by the way, that people who suffer from delayed letter-writing never get cured.

Within the minute he was through to Connecticut and he heard the voice of his brother-in-law. They knew each other because his sister had spent her honeymoon out West. All of a sudden Larry was very nervous. It hadn't occurred to him before that of course his brother-in-law had his own friends and plans for Christmas. Larry said: "Hi, Steve, it's Larry."

There was a pause. Steve was obviously wondering who Larry was. The only one he knew was a furniture consultant in a Hollywood studio. Then his voice blasted the receiver. "Larry," he yelled, "where are you?"

"In North Hollywood."

"In North Hollywood?" Another pause. "You in trouble, Larry?"

Not exactly, Larry said, with no conviction at all. He was in trouble of a sort. He was trying to invite himself, at three thousand miles, without conveying that that's what he was doing. He had no other excuse to call. It came out

fine, however, and Steve's voice was so warm and excited, and his sister's so jittery and throbbing, that Larry felt he had a home again and began to sniffle inside. He was about to hang up in gratitude and embarrassment when Steve's voice said:

"Listen, Larry. Be sure and get here Christmas Eve."

"Oh, sure," said Larry, "on the nose."

"What dya mean, on the nose?" Steve shouted. "You've never been anywhere on time in your life."

"Well, not this time. Even if we have re-takes we'll be all through by the twenty-first. I'll catch the evening plane on the twenty-third. Gets into La Guardia next morning about ten, I guess."

"Okay, I'll meet you," said Steve.

"Don't do it. I'll show you I can make it on my own hook."

Steve protested it would take at least two hours from New York and he'd have to go into the city to take a train out again. They wrangled over this for a minute or two till Larry thought of that three thousand dollars' outlay. His professional standing as a successful patient was at stake, to say nothing of his honor.

"Okay, tough guy," he said, "make a bet."

"I'll lay you a hundred to one you don't get here by midnight Christmas Eve."

"All right, I'll lay you a dollar at my end."

"Okay, my friend," roared Steve, "a hundred smackers if you get in this door by midnight."

"Whose watch do you go by these days?" Larry asked.

"Oh, that," said Steve. "Tell you what, we'll leave it up to the Congregational church here. Get here by the last stroke of twelve. After that they start in playing *The First Nowell*. It's terrible."

"It's a bet," said Larry. And so it was.

Well, the picture was finished on time, on the twenty-first, as the contract called for. Larry practiced being early. He figured how long it would take him to do his Christmas shopping and in rehearsal he did it in only fifteen minutes longer. But miss a plane by fifteen minutes, he thought, and it might just as well be a day. So he found an excuse to go to the studio and took a cab from there to the airport and checked the time. Around a large part of the rim of the widest city in the world he could do it comfortably in just under an hour. On the Freeway it might be considerably less. But it took forever to get near the Freeway, so he allowed an hour and ten or fifteen minutes. Then, as you must have guessed, fate took over.

He got an urgent call on the morning of the twenty-third. They had to reshoot one scene. It might have been any one of a score of scenes that were no concern of his. But this one concerned him, a chair, and most intimately the female star. She was a gorgeous creature, name of Gloria Love-lawn. She represented about twenty-nine per cent of the annual net profit of the studio. She was blonde and beautiful and twenty-seven, with a tiny waist, which unfortunately swerved out into a remarkable pair of hips. I say unfortunately—I wouldn't mention it here if it wasn't crucial to the story—because the scene that had misfired was one in which she had to rise from her throne (she was playing a seventeenth-century queen) and say: "Very well, then, I abdicate." That was all. It would flash on the screen for no more than ten seconds. But, as you know, such things can take all day to shoot. When they ran through the rushes an alert assistant producer who was still awake had noticed that as she got up, the chair got up too. Not for long, but long enough. It was a small point, but it was the sort of thing columnists joke about in the papers. Anyway, you can see that in an abdication scene it would be inappropriate if the throne she was leaving went along with her.

So Larry packed his bags and threw them in a cab and was over at the studio by noon. They tried it again with the same throne, but this time it came all the way with her and she retired in hysterics to her dressing-room. The direc-tor went after her. A half-hour later they emerged arm-in-arm, all serene and ready to abdicate again. It was no good. Her hips had lost none of their magnificence through hysterics. She swept her tremendous eyes on Larry and wanted to know, with a rising inflection she had learned at the Pasadena Playhouse, who had designed this chair. Larry was about to say it was genuine and had cost the studio nearly six hundred dollars. But he remembered his trip and said nothing. It was decided that they would have to have another throne. Larry canceled his flight and got a seat on another plane leaving twenty minutes after midnight. They ransacked the furniture building for an hour and a half and found nothing suitable. So Larry had to get the carpentry crew to try to accommodate the arms and seat of the same chair to the queenly shape of Gloria Lovelawn. They took the seat apart, planed the arms, stained them, nailed 'em back again. It was now ten p.m. Two hours and forty minutes to plane time, or just about an hour left.

Well, they shot it again. This time the chair creaked as she got out of it. So they did it again, keeping the microphone far back and then running it way forward for Gloria Lovelawn, as she lifted her chin, set her bosom heaving, and said superbly: "Very well, then, I abdicate." This time she had really done it. It was now ten minutes to eleven. Larry was nervous and sweating. The director knew about his trip and said at last: "I don't think you need to be around for the final take. Okay, abdicate."

Larry snatched his bag and was in a cab and at the airport about five minutes before flight time. He collapsed into his seat. And the plane wheeled around and roared up and he was on his way.

He must have dozed, but when he woke up, the little red letters about strapping your safety belt were still on.

He beckoned to the stewardess and asked how the weather was. "Clear all the way to Dallas," she said, "but we're going over the mountains." Almost as she said it they bumped a little and he looked out over the wing. It was a warm, damp moonlight night and brown, bare mountains would nose up through the haze like the hides of cattle. They pulled away from the Coast Range and suddenly there was the desert, from horizon to horizon a vast tray of sand and sage with ranges of hills snaking through it, and the single light of a ranch-house glaring into space; and every thirty miles or so the air-mail beacons winking and swinging over, and gone again, miles and miles behind in the wasteland.

He lost consciousness looking at the moonlit desert and feeling an honest love of the West. He was wakened by a red smear of light on the ceiling of the plane. He looked out and it was the dawn peering in over the foothills of the Rockies. Now you could see the dipping curves of the mountains, and the red canyons, and the highway pouring like toothpaste across the plains. It seemed no time at all before they shot out over the longest, flattest plateau, and there was a spread city down below. Down at Dallas. He looked at his flight schedule. It ought to be seven twenty-five. His watch said it was. It was balmy and hot at the airport but he had seventeen hundred miles ahead of him. There could be trouble yet.

There was. They were flying due northeast, about five hundred miles out of Dallas, and he was dozing again. Then he smelled something. Very stealthy, but warm and acrid. So did other people. And the veteran passengers looked out of one slanted eye with a casualness that meant no good. Soon there was a wisp of smoke coming up through the floor. And the stewardess put on her most flashing smile and went up front. She came back with the co-pilot and he got down on his hands and knees and pulled apart a couple of boards and there was a gush of smoke. He did something with a hand extinguisher and loped back to the cockpit. The stewardess straightened her jacket and put on the professional cordiality of a dentist. She ducked from seat to seat. They would have to land at St. Louis for a check. Nothing serious. Everyone was panicky, in that slow-motion, bunched-up way they have on a plane, and they came down at St. Louis. An hour behind time they were off again.

And now the snow came on. Hour after hour, and nothing but a white fog around you, and ice on the wings, and the engines roaring through droning modulations, and the angry jets of flame spitting out of the exhausts. They came down at Chicago. For a minute or two Larry didn't know whether this was a regular stop or not. Then they had the bad news. All eastbound planes were grounded indefinitely. Larry lived again through all the tension of the last night at the studio. He could never make it now. He thought: "Very well, then, I abdicate," and he cursed the name of Gloria Lovelawn. He thought also of his one-dollar bill, lost to Steve. It wasn't much, but it had come to mean a lot to him. He was already framing it, in his mind's eye, as the first dollar he ever earned with his reconditioned psyche.

Four hours later they were given clearance and took off in a light sleet. Larry wondered why he, unlike the people who took planes every day, always ran into these disasters.

Yet, "statistics prove . . ." He wondered how many thousands of people all over the world were up in the air having shakes and fears that would never make the statistics.

They hit an electrical storm and for ten awful minutes the plane bounced and thudded and the rains slammed at the windows. Out of the corner of his eye—he was trying not to be a sissy about airplanes—Larry saw a big taut man in his early thirties cross himself. He was across the aisle and Larry leaned over and asked him if all was well. He had to shout to make himself heard, and the big man shouted back: "No, sir. I was a bomber pilot in the war and we always prayed we'd never get into one of these things. You never know where the impulse is. If we hit the center of this thing—!" He snapped his fingers and Larry was miserable beyond telling. "Y'have to just mosey around and hope you come out," the man shouted.

At last they edged out of the storm, till there was no rain at all and the lightning flickered on the rim of the horizon. Larry looked at his watch. It was eight fifteen and at least two hours out. He didn't care much any more. Then he remembered what he was doing all this for. He had never lived with snow. Skiing up in the Sierras a time or two, sure, but he'd never gone off for a paper or a pack of cigarettes along a snowy street. He looked down and there it was all around him. Snow rumpling over the mountains. Snow in the valleys, plateaus, and slopes. Farms, river-banks, streets, cities, villages—a planet of snow. He smiled at the sharp purple shadow of the plane skimmering across fields and bending over white hills. He was still watching this shadow and the mild moon when the safety-belt and no-smoking signs went on again. Ahead he could make out a city glow and the twinkle of a river. The stewardess said: "We shall land in five minutes." His watch said ten twenty. He began to shake with excitement. There was a bare sport-ing chance. Sudenly to the south the jewel of Manhattan and the lines of light down the avenues, and then a swarm of suburbs, and the banking, and the bump and rumble of the landing.

Outside the main building he saw a little fat cabdriver picking his teeth and leaning against his cab. It was ten thirty-five. The man lifted an index finger and Larry hurled his bags inside and dived in after them. Larry coughed and leaned back. "New Bethlehem, Connecticut," he said.

The cabdriver swiveled as if he'd been slapped.

"You mean south of Kent? Are you kiddin'? That's a two-hour drive, it's eighty-some miles."

"I know, I know," said Larry, still catching his breath.

"That's gonna run up to twenny, twenny-fie dollars maybe."

"I'll give you fifty if you make it."

"That would just about cover it, mister—I use gasoline on the way back, y'know."

"Make it seventy dollars, if we can only get moving."

"Cash or by check, maybe?" looking right ahead, not doing a thing with gears.

Larry whipped out his wallet and took out two new twenty-dollar bills and three tens. He crouched forward and rustled them crisply in the driver's ear.

"Okay," the driver sang out, "you're the doctor. She must be some babe."

"Fine," said Larry, "but let's get going. Whaddya say?"

"You pay the fine if I'm nabbed?"

"I will, I will," Larry shouted. And the driver pulled into first and they were off.

"Any particular route you have in mind?"

"No, I'm a stranger in these parts. Whatever you say. But we have to make it by midnight."

"You got hopes," said the driver, and they started out on a weaving network of parkways, over a long bridge, up by a river and again onto a spinning parkway, whose surface was the only hard dry thing in a rolling landscape of snow and trees. They moved up from fifty to sixty, from sixty-five to seventy, and then they heard the low fatal whine of a police car. It was not a police car. It was an ambulance and it flew past them and its red tail-light went out like a cinder.

They unwound themselves by a clover-leaf off the parkway and were soon swishing across country up roads thick with foliage and snow frozen on the branches. It was eleven thirty-five. But Larry forgot the tension of the chase for the moment in looking at the paradise around him. He might have been in heaven or getting his first view of the Grand Canyon. The straight, small fields glimmering with snow, the white houses, the little hills lying snugly against the rivers like big sleeping bears. Maybe that was Bear Mountain he'd heard about. It was not. But it could have been. There are scores of mountains called Bear Mountain in New England and they are well named.

They came at last down a long hillside and through a little valley ahead of them saw a white village. Through the snow-laden trees a white spire rose up and touched the stars. That must be the Congregational church. At the moment he saw it Larry looked down at his watch. It said six minutes before midnight. But then across the quiet valley he heard the dreadful sound: the first chimes of

twelve. They were a couple of miles away and the chimes struck and shivered as the cab's tires squealed round the lanes. As they came into the main street of the town the chimes took a deep wheezy breath and began to play a tune. A stop light turned red and they sat waiting for it. Larry heard *The First Nowell* clanging uncertainly through many a half-note and shaky tone. They hailed a man far gone in liquor but he was a native and he knew the house. They pulled up with a jerk outside it. Larry stuffed the seventy dollars into the cabdriver's waiting hand, murmured his thanks and a Merry Christmas, and walked with all the time in the world up the path. Before he was there the door opened and his sister was around his neck. They both cried, but for very different reasons.

Steve put on a rather heavy show of wanting to be charitable but he made it plain to the adolescent brother-in-law that a bet was a bet all right. The three of them embraced and said it was a shame; and Larry now included his old psychiatrist in the curses he flung at the memory of Gloria Lovelawn.

*   *   *

There is not much more to this sad story. It would have been all over if Steve had not said, with a suspiciously theatrical gesture, that he had to listen to a radio commercial. He leaned over and switched it on. A clear baritone, an oily, velvet-smooth announcer's voice, announced: "In ten seconds from now you will hear the chimes of Trinity Church in New York City ring in the holy day." Larry looked up wild with disbelief and then the bells chimed and the holy day came in, as always, with a roar of drunken shouting from a crowd in the studio, or on a record, or in Times Square, it didn't matter where.

"The clock in the Congregational church," said Steve with enormous boredom, "has been six minutes fast for a hundred and sixty years, and no old family around here will ever let you fix it. I thought I'd give you six minutes' leeway, for free."

He held out a hundred-dollar bill, the first Larry had ever seen.

That is the end of the story, except for people who may still have any interest at all in Larry's pursuit of his origins.

They cracked a bottle of champagne (non-Californian), and then another. They were still up an hour later and they heard Christmas come in over the radio in Chicago. Larry was beyond the reach of fear by now and they sat up till three o'clock, for old times' sake, to hear Christmas come in in California. They heard it. The same velvet voice, it

might have been the same man, the same raucous cheers, and the band music. Just as they were about to switch off, a commentator whom Larry knew slightly came on with news flashes from the studios. The first item came over on the California midnight clear: "Flash! Gloria Lovelawn, the famous movie star, is resting comfortably in Heavenly Pines Hospital after an accident that befell her yesterday in the last few minutes of shooting on her nearly completed starring vehicle, *The Queen Stands Down*. Miss Lovelawn was engaged on her last scene when the throne she was sitting in collapsed. Miss Lovelawn suffered severe lacerations of the-er-lower back. The final retake is expected to be held up for two or three weeks."

At a single bound Larry and Steve went off into a very brisk rumba and the three of them danced till dawn.

The studio is still looking for Larry but it has not found him. Larry grew even fonder of the snow than he'd expected and he decided to settle in the East. His brother-in-law got him a job designing working models for television advertisements. His masterpiece was one showing a parade of courtiers, dressed up like cigarettes, attending the abdication of the Emperor Napoleon (a puppet) in favor of "Black Prince—the KING-of-Cigarettes."

So Larry is back with his forefathers, giving revenue to the tobacco company on weekdays and on Sundays giving glory to God in the 1790 Congregational church with the obstinate clock.

THREE

AMODERN American poet has written: "From the
new earth the dead return no more," meaning that
in America there are no ghost stories. Is that so? Well, I
beg to amend the record and tell you what can happen,
what did happen two hundred years ago, and again only
one year ago, in a country place up the Hudson which was

settled by Dutchmen who brought over and transformed the oldest legend about Santa Claus.

In the seventeenth century the Dutch crews who used to drop anchor in the Hudson heard about some buried treasure. For several generations headstrong men would go out digging for it in the near-by hills. The man I have in mind was one Rambout Van Dam, who got obsessed with gold and nearly lost his daughters. That may sound like a contradiction in terms. I had better explain it gently by beginning at the beginning.

If anybody had asked Rambout if he was a good father he would have laughed aloud. He had three adored daughters, one beautiful, one very homely, and one like you and me. They were all, however, intelligent, which is much more of a threat to parenthood than the other vices. Ram Van Dam was a gay dog in a quiet way, and a little less quiet after his wife died. He had a fine streak of curiosity, which two of his daughters inherited. The beautiful one didn't need to. All the curiosity came her way.

Well, Ram sat and moped for a while as a widower. And then he took to rowing up the Hudson every Saturday night across a fine stretch of water called the Tappan Zee. He would tie up and tramp off to a tavern and a few hours later would untie and have quite a time of it rowing back home.

One night at the tavern he heard about the buried treasure. And in the next year, having a small income from farming land his wife had left him, he had a lot of time on his hands to mooch around for gold. Maybe he was told, or maybe he just connected the buried treasure with the place he'd heard about, but he grew convinced as the months went by that the Rockland Hills were the place to explore. One summer and fall he spent almost every day there and the week before Christmas he had done nothing about chopping down a Christmas tree or preparing to make merry. So far as his daughters could see, he didn't mean to.

The more he went away from home, the more he made it up to his guilty conscience by being stricter and stricter with his daughters. He had the sense to see that they were growing and ripening before his eyes. He noticed that the beautiful one was always seeming to run into young men she knew, either in the village store or sometimes nearer home. So he gave out an order: no men, no visitors, whenever he went away. He barred the storm windows and he locked the doors and took the key away with him.

This Christmas week, two hundred years ago, he went off as usual with his rowboat and a pail and a spade. Christmas Eve came in with dull grey skies, but he rowed off just the same. He didn't get very far. The skies lowered and the snow came down, and he put into a little cove and waited to sit the storm out. But the snow came down heavier and in the middle of the afternoon he pushed his rowboat out into the Hudson again and bent before the whirling storm and pulled for home. He forgot all about the buried treasure. He began to get maudlin as he thought of the locked-up treasure of his daughters. As he rowed he sweated and as he sweated he wept. He had never loved his daughters so much in his life, now that he seemed near to never seeing them again. He could see no landing lights anywhere across the dizzy falling snow. And there came to him a quick, horrible fear.

His daughters had been very quiet and complacent that morning. They had done everything he asked. His crullers were baked when he came downstairs. His tea was hot. His cheese was pungent. A little pot of rum was already poured for him. His daughters had never behaved so like good daughters in the storybooks. He was an experienced parent after all, and he knew this was a bad sign.

Soon the night came on with that terrible gentleness of any night that brings disaster. He knew his own landing-place without stopping to think but he saw no glimmer of light between the pines. He tied up the boat with shaking fingers and climbed up the bank and plodded knee-deep through the snow. He hadn't even noticed that the snow had stopped. But it was deep and very still now. And what was worse, the great looming ghost of his house was still and dark.

Was it possible that his beloved daughters had gone looking for him and suffered he daren't think what sort of fate? He pulled out the great key to the front door. But he didn't need it and he knew as he chattered there that

he might never need it again. The door was ajar. It creaked
as he pushed it, and he heard it in his head as a squeaking
demon laugh, a sort of sick chuckle from another world.
He lit the lamp in the hallway and shouted out their names.
There was no answer, no light, no sound but the door
creaking back with a sigh. "Gone, old man, gone for good,"
the door said.

He ran into the living-room and lit another lamp. As the
flame leaped up, he saw under it a piece of paper. He did
not have to read what had been written down on it so
painstakingly. He saw only the words: "and so, dear
Father, and on account of this unhappy neglect"; and he
jumped two lines to read: "have taken the stagecoach to
New York City, there, as we intend, to abandon ourselves
to a life of merry shame."

He fell in silly sobs over the torn page. After a while he heard a church bell strike and he moved fast. He tossed off a noggin of rum. He threw on a greatcoat and plodded back to the stable and saddled his horse. He took a lantern. He knew the roads as well as any farmer in the Hudson Valley and it was his guess that the stage had plunged into a snowdrift. It left, he remembered, at four o'clock. And it was now eight. He rode off through the snow into the dark.

He was luckily right. He found the stage five miles down the road, with the passengers all gone to an inn two miles away. He turned and rode on. Not to sicken you further, he found his daughters. They were surrounded by sturdy, cheerful-looking men and they were drinking hot rum

toddies, with cinnamon sticks stuck shamelessly in big pewter mugs. It took a little time and a private interview in a back room to get the daughters weeping. But they wept copiously, not because they had recanted about the prospect of a life of merry shame, but because they had never seen their father look so old, so red in the nose, so pathetic. I mean, they had never seen him cry.

He borrowed another horse and galloped back home with them. By the time they were home they promised him everlasting obedience and all sorts of virtues he hadn't so far noticed in them. But he looked them in the eye and they looked him straight back. And he knew that New York was still a pleasing prospect and a date in their diaries. They went sorrowfully to bed.

They were all asleep when the church bell struck a deep, challenging, throbbing twelve. If they had not all been so exhausted, they would have died of fright in their beds. For there was a strange ringing of little bells across the fields, followed soon by a scraping sound at the chimney, and a dislodged brick fell down the roofing and thudded into the snow. The living-room, and the tree they had dragged in and put up, were crackling with light. Then the light went out and the chimneystack made the same scraping sound, and the bells vanished across the fields.

[*51*]

Next morning when they came down, at the foot of the tree were three packages. They each contained a dowry. This was enough to abolish the thrilling prospect of a life of merry shame. The very plain one married the stagecoachman. And the in-between one married her dowry. And the beautiful one took her time and married the Mayor of New York City and settled down to a life of merry respectability. But Ram Van Dam never again went rowing up the Hudson for gold. The word got around that a stranger had come on Christmas Eve and restored the old man to his daughters, and vice versa. Everyone in the Hudson Valley the next year put up a tree and left little baskets and other suitable containers for dowries for their own daughters. For a time they called the invisible stranger simply The Stranger, but since he came on Saint Nicholas' Eve they got to calling him at first Nick; then, when he left no dowries, Old Nick; then Saint 'Claus, and finally Santa Claus, a horrid Americanism that the rest of the world first execrated and then, as is its custom, adopted. Such dreadful anxieties were set up in the valley children that a few kindly parents started sneaking in bits of money and little presents to put under the tree at midnight. This too got to be taken for granted. So that today many a grumpy father, going off to empty his earnings on a pile of presents, refers to Santa Claus simply as That Dam Ghost.

This might have been all there is to tell of this Hudson Valley legend if life ended as the fairy stories do. But I regret to say that Ram Van Dam again got to taking his daughters for granted. And one fine Saturday night he rowed up the river and across the waters of the Tappan Zee. He carried his pail and spade with him. We do not know for certain what happened to him, but he never came back. And if you go down to the Hudson shore on Christmas Eve, and however crisp and bright the night, you will see nothing; but you will hear all night long, if you care to stay, the faint splashing, the weary dipping of oars, up and down the waters of the Tappan Zee.

This was the fate of the father who took his children for granted and tried the fatal, though familiar, experiment of "molding their characters."

There was a further warning given to all of us last year when a certain Raymond Van Dam, who lives in those parts, threatened to repeat the error of his ancestor's way. He is an upright, cultivated man, but of the sort who has been educated about two degrees (A.B. and Ph.D.) above his intelligence. I hate to bring nationalism into this but it will explain a very eccentric trait of his: he was half-English and hated American radio. He too had three daughters. From their earliest childhood he banned all radio sets from his house. Like many another tyrant masquerading as a "sensitive man," he thought this would give his children no taste for the stuff. But he was wrong, and he learned it just in time.

A few weeks before Christmas, while his daughters were in school, he saw a postcard addressed to the beautiful one on the letter tray in the hall. Same house, by the way. As he shuffled through his own mail, the postcard fell face-

down. He was, as I say, a moral man. But he believed there was a special dispensation that made it all right to read other people's postcards. He read it. It was from a theatrical agency. It said that a television network had agreed to the proposition of the three girls to take an audition for a sister act, a close-harmony trio! Mr. Raymond Van Dam replaced the letter. And he did not go out to saddle his horse. But he moved as fast as his ancestor. He got out his car and drove into Tarrytown and headed for a big, bright department store.

On Christmas Eve the bells were heard again, and the scraping sound, and a brick fell off the roof. Next morning, when the girls came down, they found to their astonishment three huge packages. One was a television set, one was

a radio, and the third was a phonograph with a three-speed player.

They now watch television every night and play the radio and phonograph every morning. Mr. Van Dam has never had it so peaceful.

Mr. Van Dam received the embraces of his daughters all day long. But he had a testy gleam in his eye. And the next day he wrote a tart letter to a certain doctor friend— a friend no more—a psychiatrist attached to the World Health Organization. This doctor, I understand, is trying to get the United Nations to agree to undertake a propaganda campaign to belittle, deplore, and in time abolish Santa Claus from the national customs and the folklore of all the signatory nations. Santa Claus, this psychiatrist says, is a dangerous sentimental father-figure, who is expected to satisfy "unreasonable wants," and who by that very expectation delays "the necessary adjustment of the pre-adolescent child to the world of reality."

Did I say Mr. Van Dam wrote a letter? I'm sorry. His temper was much too short for that. He sent a telegram. It read:

MERRY CHRISTMAS STOP YOU ARE A DAMN FOOL STOP
VAN DAM.

This book is set on the Intertype in a face called *Weiss*. The late E. R. Weiss said about his type design: "I trust . . . that these letters can rightfully assume their place in the unbroken line of traditional letter design, and yet they are a product of our own time, as each generation alters old forms to suit new needs. . . ."

The type was set by *The Composing Room, Inc.*, New York. The book was reproduced in photo-offset by *Reehl Litho Company, Inc.*, New York, and bound by *H. Wolff*, New York.